The Lighthouse People

Susan Paris

illustrated by Denise Durkin

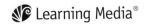
Learning Media®

Contents

8:00 p.m.

The night of the big storm, Dad told us the bad news. We'd just finished dinner and were sitting around. We were all a little on edge.

Storms are a regular thing when you live in a lighthouse, but this one was something else. Every few minutes, the building shuddered like a rocket about to lift off.

"Kids, there's something we need to talk about," Dad said, a grim look on his face. His eyes met Mom's, and I knew then that it was serious. "Lately, there's been talk about automating the lighthouse," he said. I looked at Mom, but she was plucking at the tablecloth. She'd been checking the generator that afternoon – the weather forecast had made her nervous – and there was grease under her nails. Dad reached for her hand.

"Mom and I didn't want you to worry until we knew more," Dad continued, "but it's not looking too good." My dinner churned in my stomach, and I brushed some crumbs into a pile so that I wouldn't cry.

"They can't make us leave. This is our home," Tim protested. "They can't – can they, Becca?" he said, looking at me like I could help. I shrugged.

"I've tried to convince them they need us, Tim," Dad said gently, "but it all comes down to money – that's the bottom line. Solar power and batteries are much cheaper than people. We have to face facts."

The facts weren't too good. Over the last few years, many lighthouse keepers had lost their jobs. We knew families who had moved away. Some had even gone to the cities, where they lived in tiny apartments with no yard. I'd been to a big city before, and there was nothing to do except shop and watch movies. I didn't want that kind of life. Most of the lighthouse people who'd been forced to leave didn't want to live like that, either. Somehow, I'd never really believed it could happen to us.

Mom pushed back her chair. "A tanker's due past tonight, and this storm's getting worse." She still wasn't looking at anyone. "I'm going to listen to the marine forecast." She went into the radio room, softly closing the door behind her.

Tim began pulling his ear. He did that when he was upset. "Everything will be OK," Dad said. "You'll see."

11:00 p.m.

Later, I lay awake for a long time. The rain
hammered against my window, and I stared out
at the black night. I never pulled the curtains
when there was a storm. I was too scared I'd
miss something. Besides, I liked watching
the regular flash of our light interrupting
the darkness.

The shrieking roar of the wind and the ocean filled my room, their sounds difficult to tell apart. The waves would be breaking much higher than usual. In the morning, our beach would be covered in seaweed and driftwood. Sometimes, the debris was so thick, you couldn't see the sand. We'd be able to build a hut, then go treasure hunting. Some amazing things washed up on the beach during a storm.

Last month, Tim found a bike. Dad said that sailors use them to get around on the oil tankers. The parts were badly rusted, but Tim was using them to make a sculpture.

Much later, I heard my parents come up
to bed. They'd been talking for a long time.
I concentrated on sleep, wishing that my
unhappy thoughts would go away.

1:00 a.m.

Next thing I knew, Dad was shaking my shoulder. "Becca, wake up. The power's out, and we can't get the emergency generator to work. I need you to help."

Downstairs, I lit candles and stayed near the radio while Mom and Dad ran between the shed and the workshop. Our power came from the mainland, and we hadn't used the generator for years. It was meant to be a backup during an emergency. Until tonight, there'd never been one.

The storm was worse than ever, and I worried about my parents outside. The lighthouse shook constantly, and Tim and I had to shout to be heard.

"There's a tanker near the reef," Tim yelled, "and Dad can't fix the generator." His small face was pale in the dim light.

"He will," I said. "You should put your sweater on." The furnace was out, and it was cold. I turned on the gas stove to heat some water and tried not to think about the tanker.

Over the years, lots of ships had sunk on the reef, and many sailors had drowned. That was why the lighthouse had been built. I wondered how many people were on the tanker.

Mom gave me a tight smile when I handed her some coffee. I'd spilled half of it running to the shed through the rain. She took a sip, careful to keep the flashlight shining on the generator. Dad was hunched over it, mumbling to himself, his face creased with concentration. I put his coffee on the windowsill and stood quietly watching.

We weren't usually allowed in the generator shed. Dad didn't like us near the diesel. Large cans were stacked neatly in the far corner, and the walls were lined with equipment: spare life jackets, fishing nets, buoys, batteries, an extra radio … all the things that kept us safe on our rock. I took a deep breath. I liked the smells in there – musty and kind of oily, with the strong, salty smell of the ocean.

Dad straightened up, frowning, and pulled his knit hat lower. "I can't figure out what's wrong," he sighed. "Have you kids been playing in here – fooling around with something?"

"No," I replied, indignant. "You told us not to." But Dad was reaching for his wrench, no longer listening.

"You should be keeping an eye on Tim," Mom said, changing the subject. "Besides, you're soaking." She was right – I was freezing, but I didn't want to leave. Mom guessed what I was thinking.

"I've radioed the Coast Guard. The oil tanker will be fine." We both knew that our light was still needed, but I just nodded.

An hour later, nothing had changed. I'd
made more coffee so I could stand near the
warm stove, and Tim had drawn a ship in a
storm. He refused to go back to bed. I sat by
the window, hoping to spot the tanker, but it
was impossible to see.

It was weird looking out over the dark water without our light sweeping across the waves. It was even weirder thinking that soon I might never see the light again. I suddenly felt angry. I'd lived in the lighthouse most of my life. Mom and Dad homeschooled us, and supplies were delivered every two weeks. We had everything we needed. How could they make us leave?

"Becca, is there oil on that tanker?" asked Tim. Like me, he'd seen pictures of seabirds and seals after an oil spill.

"Probably," I said, "but I'm sure the captain has traveled this route hundreds of times. He'll know about the reef."

Tim pressed his nose against the glass. "I hope so."

3:00 a.m.

The door banged loudly, and Mom stood
dripping on the mat. "I need a hot water
bottle. Dad's hands are so cold he can't work.
He keeps dropping his tools." I jumped up,
glad I'd been heating so much water. Mom saw
Tim's worried face and smiled at him. "Some
towels would be great, Tim." He looked proud
to be included and ran upstairs, returning
with an enormous pile that he could only just
see over.

Suddenly, Dad appeared.
Something stiff and furry
dangled from his hand.
He threw an arm around
Mom. "What's that?"
she cried, leaping away.

"A rat," said Dad happily.
"It had chewed through the
wires. Don't worry – it's been
dead for hours."

"Are you sure?" Tim asked.

"Absolutely," said Dad. "This guy's history."
Tim looked a little disappointed.

"So, the light's working?" I asked.

"Sure is." Dad smiled. "Is there more coffee?"

Before I did anything, I had to check for
myself. The light was a bright glow, and I could
just make out the tanker. It was a tiny speck on
the horizon. No one on board would ever know
we'd worked all night to keep them safe.

"If we tell the Coast Guard what we've done,
maybe they'll let us stay," I suggested.

"It's not that simple," said Dad. "I wish it were."

The ocean still roared, but the rain was a steadier beat when we finally went to bed. For the second time that night, I couldn't sleep. I was thinking about telling my friend Jane what had happened. She lived on the mainland and was always telling me I have a strange life. Her family calls us the lighthouse people. I've told Jane that maybe one day I'll want to live on the mainland. But somehow, I doubt it.

From People to Power

Early last century, there were around fifteen hundred lighthouses in the United States. They used lamps that burned oil and kerosene. The lighthouse keepers lit the lamps, trimmed the wicks, kept the mirrors and windows of the lighthouse clean, made sure there was enough fuel, and rescued shipwrecked sailors. It was a full-time job, and most lighthouse keepers lived in or near the lighthouse.

During the 1940s, ships began using radar to navigate, and lighthouses became less important. Many were shut down. Around the same time, electric motors began to replace lighthouse keepers. Today, nearly all of the three hundred lighthouses in the United States, and the 275 in Canada, are automatic.

The first lighthouse was built in the Egyptian city of Alexandria between 283 and 246 B.C.

The Fresnel Lens

The light from a modern lighthouse comes from a lamp that has a very powerful bulb. Many lighthouses also use a special lens that was invented in 1822 by French scientist Augustin Fresnel. This lens uses triangular pieces of glass called prisms to direct the rays of light from the lamp into a strong beam. Light from a Fresnel lens can be seen 20 miles (32 kilometers) out at sea.

Most lighthouses shine in two directions, like the one shown in the picture. The lamp also rotates, sweeping the ocean with a strong beam of light. This means that every few seconds, the light can be seen from anywhere at sea.